Contents

Teachers' notes

Aims of this book

The aims of this book are:
• to offer children a range of situations in which to develop confidence as speakers and listeners;
• to give children a variety of opportunities to work with different partners;
• to give scope for important role-playing experience;
• to encourage imagination through play and improvised drama;
• to offer purposeful activities in which to develop pupils' power of concentration, grasp of turn-taking and ability to hold the attention of their listeners;
• to enable pupils to listen and respond to stories and rhymes;
• to prompt them to tell and retell familiar stories.

Developing language skills

Language skills and the ability to communicate effectively underpin success in all curriculum areas. For this reason the National Curriculum places considerable emphasis upon pupils' success in speaking and listening, irrespective of their initial competence or home language. In the busy classroom, it can be difficult for the teacher to ensure that all children have equality of experience through which they can develop as speakers and listeners.

Equality of opportunity

It can happen that some articulate children dominate the 'talk time' in the classroom. This can prevent the more reticent child from making oral contributions. Some children are confident at talking to teachers and other adults, and this may lead the teacher to assume that the same child is as successful a communicator with his or her own peers, which is not always the case. The children who are good at talking to the teacher may find it difficult to grasp turn-taking and the ability to voice disagreement courteously when talking with their peers.

Similarly, some children who are shy at participating in group activities, show through their other school work that, although they may not have spoken very much, they have listened attentively – and this skill is easily overlooked. For this reason, the teacher needs to plan situations and activities which provide equality of opportunity for all children.

The activities in this book focus upon two of the aspects of Speaking and Listening, responding to literature and nursery rhymes, and talking with others in response to a range of activities including drama. Many of the activities require the children to play rhyming games as the ability to recognise rhyme aurally enhances children's ability to read and write.

The structured tasks present the pupils with opportunities to work co-operatively with a partner. It is advisable to keep a record of the partners that children select as otherwise there is a tendency for children to always opt to work with a preferred friend. Whilst this can, on occasions, be a very profitable working arrangement, it may affect the children's range of talking and learning experiences.

The photocopiable activities will prompt purposeful talk and teachers can ensure that all children receive the same encouragement to develop their speaking and listening skills. These activities should also enable the teacher to keep a record of each child's speaking and listening opportunities and performance.

Notes on individual activities

Pages 5-6: Make a mask

These masks, simple to colour and cut out, are an excellent way to encourage children to talk in role. The Programme of Study for Key Stage 1, Speaking and Listening, encourages children to take part in drama activities, using language appropriate to a role or situation. For this activity four children work together in each group. In order to support children's language in this role-playing activity, it is best to ensure that the children are familiar with the story of Goldilocks and the Three Bears. The teacher might like to keep the dialogue on task by taking the role of a narrator. Some less confident talkers in the class might benefit from discussing the role before enacting it, eg, 'What did Daddy Bear say?' 'What did Baby Bear say?'

It is quite possible to extend this role-play fiction-recall activity into a prediction game by asking the children to think what the characters might have said after the end of the story, eg, 'What did Mummy Bear say after Goldilocks had run off?' Some confident groups of children might like to perform their play for others to watch.

Pages 7-11: Spot the difference

For these activities children work with a partner. First remind the children of the principle of a spot-the-difference activity. They should search for the differences individually and circle each difference as they find it and number it. When both children in each pair have found all the differences they should compare the order in which these differences were found. When they have compared notes they could colour the pictures.

Extension activity: encourage the children to use the pictures to tell one of the well-known tales.

Pages 11-12: What's wrong?

For these activities children work with a partner. They should examine the pictures closely to discover what is wrong in each picture. Before beginning the activity check that the children are familiar with the two nursery rhymes 'Humpty Dumpty' and 'Jack and Jill'. The partners work together to discuss what is wrong in each picture. Encourage the partners to take it in turn to point out the errors. In this way each child gets an equal opportunity to be involved in the activity.

Extension activity: the children could choose their favourite picture and colour it in.

Pages 13-14: Retelling well-known tales

In these activities well-known tales are depicted in each set of four pictures. Children work with a partner. One child tells the story to his or her partner using the pictures as a prompt. Then the second child tells the story depicted by the second set of pictures. In order to make the most of this oral story-telling it is advisable to ensure that the children are familiar with the plots and also to remind them of the language of well-known tales, e.g., 'Once upon a time...', 'Up and up and up he climbed...', 'Fee, fi, fo, fum, I smell the blood of an Englishman', 'The cruel step-mother...', 'The ugly sisters...', 'Poor Cinderella could not go to the ball...', 'Be sure to return by midnight'. The children could listen to a recording of the relevant fairy-tale as preparation for their own retelling. At the end of the story some children might like to record their retelling.

Pages 15-16: Acting out well-known tales

Through drama and role-play children can gain confidence in oral language. In these activities small groups of children (three to four) can retell amongst themselves the well-known tales. Some children will need to have the tale retold or reread to them before they engage in their own retelling. Once the participants are confident in the retelling they can choose one of the pictures to act out the scene for others to guess.

Page 17: Make an old rhyme

Rhyme is an important acquisition in the developing skills of the young reader. This activity has two well-known rhymes ('Hickory, dickory, dock' and 'Hey diddle diddle') for children to complete. The missing words are in a bank at the end of each rhyme. Each word also has a small illustration, so that even those children who cannot read the words can participate in this rhyming activity. Once the children have filled in the missing rhyming words, encourage them to choose one of the rhymes to learn by heart.

Page 18: Make a new rhyme

This activity is exactly the same as the above, except that the rhyme will not be familiar to the children. Some children may need help from an adult or another child to read the rhyme for the first time, but all should be able to identify the missing words in picture form and then to add them to fill the gaps in the rhyme. Some children might like to learn these rhymes by heart.

Pages 19-20: What will happen next?

For this activity children work with a partner. They take it in turns to describe a picture, i.e., the first child describes picture 1 and the second child describes picture 2. Together they imagine what might be drawn in picture 4. Once they have discussed their suggestions, each child can draw their own ending to the story. It might be very useful to tape-record the children's responses.

Pages 21-22: Make a puppet

For this activity children will need to work in groups of four. Like making masks, using simple puppets gives young children a stimulus for purposeful talk. First ensure that all the children are familiar with the story of the Billy Goats Gruff. Children should then choose a character and colour it in. Those children who are able should be encouraged to cut out on their own their chosen character. Paste the cut-out paper characters on to card and fix a short length of garden cane to the centre of the back of the puppet. The children can then hold on to the cane and use it to move their puppet character.

Page 23: Find the rhyme – 1

For this activity children work with a partner. Each child has a copy of the page in front of them. The first child chooses one of the pictures and puts number 1 in the top right-hand corner. He or she then says the name of the object and the partner must find the word on the page which rhymes with the word they have heard. The partner then puts number 1 in the top right-hand corner of the rhyming word. Then the second child selects a picture and puts number 2 in the top right-hand corner and says the word for the first player, who in turn must find the picture which rhymes with that word. The game continues until all the pictures have been matched with a rhyme. The players then compare their results to see if the matching numbers are indeed rhyming words.

Page 24: Find the rhyme – 2

This activity is played in exactly the same way as Find the rhyme (1).

Page 25: Build a nursery rhyme

The nursery rhyme 'One, two, buckle my shoe', is jumbled up on the page. Children work with a partner to cut out and reassemble the rhyme. Once the rhyme has been put together in the correct order and pasted on to a piece of paper, encourage the children to learn the rhyme by heart with one partner saying the numbers, i.e., 'One, two' and the other saying the verse 'Buckle my shoe'. When they have said the rhyme once, they can swap roles.

Page 26: Rebus rhyme – 1

For this activity children work with a partner to say the rhyme by reading the words and the pictures. Once they can say the rhyme confidently, they can rebuild the rhyme from the jumbled lines on the bottom half of the page. These need to be cut out and then pasted down in the correct order.

Page 27: Rebus rhyme – 2

This activity is exactly the same as Rebus rhyme – 1.
Extension activity: children might like to devise their own rebus version of a nursery rhyme.

Page 28: Choose-your-own fairy story

For this activity children work with a partner. Each child looks at the words and pictures and decides how they would like to invent their own story. When they have decided which pictures they want to use to complete their story, they colour in just those pictures. When they have coloured in one picture per line they can read their own version to their partner. Children may enjoy recording their version on to a cassette.

Page 29: Odd one out – 1

For this activity children work with a partner or with an adult. The adult reads out each line of rhyming words in turn and the child listens for the one which does not rhyme. The child should write the 'odd' word on a separate piece of paper. When all the words have been read the child can check the answers. This game encourages careful listening and for this reason the child should not be spotting the 'odd one out' visually, but *hearing* the difference.

Page 30: Odd one out – 2

This activity is played in exactly the same way as Odd one out – 1.

Page 31: My favourite story

The National Curriculum encourages children to reflect on what they have read. This activity invites children to fill in details of a story they have read. This can then become the basis for discussion about the book and help children to structure their responses. Children should be encouraged to jot down notes rather than write at length, as the page should be a prompt for discussion rather than a writing exercise.

National Curriculum: English

The activities in this book support the following requirements of the PoS for KS1 for the National Curriculum for English:

Speaking and Listening
- Pupils should be given opportunities to talk for a range of purposes, including:
  - telling stories, both real and imagined; imaginative play and drama; reading and listening to nursery rhymes and poetry, learning some by heart; reading aloud;
  - exploring, developing and clarifying ideas; predicting outcomes and discussing possibilities;
  - describing events, observations and experiences; making simple, clear explanations of choices; giving reasons for opinions and actions;
- Pupils should be given opportunities to consider how talk is influenced by the purpose and by the intended audience. These opportunities should include work in groups of different sizes;
- Pupils should be taught to listen carefully and to show their understanding of what they see and hear by making relevant comments;
- Pupils should be encouraged to participate in drama activities, improvisation and performances of varying kinds, using language appropriate to a role or situation;
- To communicate effectively, pupils should be taught the importance of language that is clear, fluent and interesting. Building on their previous experience, pupils should be encouraged to speak with confidence, making themselves clear through organising what they say and choosing words with precision. They should be taught to incorporate relevant detail in explanations, descriptions and narratives, and to distinguish between the essential and the less important, taking into account the needs of their listeners. Pupils should be taught conventions of discussion and conversation, *eg taking turns in speaking,* and how to structure their talk in ways that are coherent and understandable;
- Pupils should be encouraged to listen with growing attention and concentration... They should use talk to develop their thinking and extend their ideas in the light of discussion;
- Pupils' vocabulary should be extended through activities that encourage their interest in words, including exploration and discussion of:
  - word games;
  - characteristic language in storytelling, *eg 'Once upon a time'.*

Reading
- Pupils should be introduced to and should read information, both in print and on screen;
- The materials read and discussed should be used to stimulate pupils' imagination and enthusiasm. They should include:
  - language with recognisable repetitive patterns, rhyme and rhythm;
- Pupils should be ... made aware of the sounds of spoken language in order to develop phonological awareness. They should also be taught to use various approaches to word identification and recognition;
- Pupils should be taught to use ... phonic knowledge, focusing on the relationships between print symbols and sound patterns. Opportunities should be given for:
  - recognising... sound patterns and rhyme.

Writing
- Pupils should be helped to understand the value of writing as a means of remembering, communicating, organising and developing ideas and information;
- Pupils should be given opportunities to write in response to a variety of stimuli.

Scottish 5-14 Curriculum: English language

Attainment outcome	Strand	Attainment target	Level
Listening	Knowledge of language	Knowledge of term 'rhyme'.	B
	Listening in groups	Listen and respond by contributing.	A
	Listening in order to respond to texts	Listen to a simple story, poem or dramatic text and respond.	A
Talking	Talking in groups	Talk to others in a group led by an adult.	A
	Talking about texts	Talk about a simple story, poem or dramatic text revealing some reaction to one aspect of it.	A

See page 32 for Scottish 5-14 Curriculum continued and Northern Ireland Curriculum links

Make a mask

Make a mask

Spot the difference

The Enormous Turnip

● Look carefully at the two pictures. Can you find ten differences?

Spot the difference

The Gingerbread Man

● Look carefully at the two pictures. Can you find ten differences?

Spot the difference

Little Red Riding Hood

● Look carefully at the two pictures. Can you find ten differences?

Spot the difference

The Billy Goats Gruff

● Look carefully at the two pictures. Can you find ten differences?

What's wrong?

Humpty Dumpty

● Look carefully at the picture. Can you spot ten things wrong?

What's wrong?

Jack and Jill

● Look carefully at the picture. Can you spot ten things wrong?

Retelling well-known tales

Jack and the Beanstalk

● Look at the four pictures. Tell the story from the pictures and then finish the story on your own.

Retelling well-known tales

Cinderella

● Look at the four pictures. Tell the story from the pictures and then finish the story on your own.

Retelling well-known tales

Jack and the Beanstalk

● Look at the four pictures. Tell the story from the pictures and then finish the story on your own.

Retelling well-known tales

Cinderella

● Look at the four pictures. Tell the story from the pictures and then finish the story on your own.

Acting out well-known tales

The Ugly Duckling

● Look at the pictures. Tell each other the story. Act it out for your friends.

Acting out well-known tales

The Little Red Hen

● Look at the four pictures. Act out the story for your friends.

Make an old rhyme

● Put the words in the spaces to make the rhyme.

mouse

Hickory, dickory, dock,
The _____ ran up the clock.
The _____ struck one,
The _____ ran down.
Hickory, dickory, dock.

clock

mouse

● Put the words in the spaces to make the rhyme.

cow

spoon

moon

dog

Hey diddle, diddle,
The _____ and the fiddle,
The _____ jumped over the _____
The little _____ laughed to see such fun
And the dish ran away with the _____

cat

● Now choose a rhyme and learn it.

Make a new rhyme

● Write the words in the spaces.

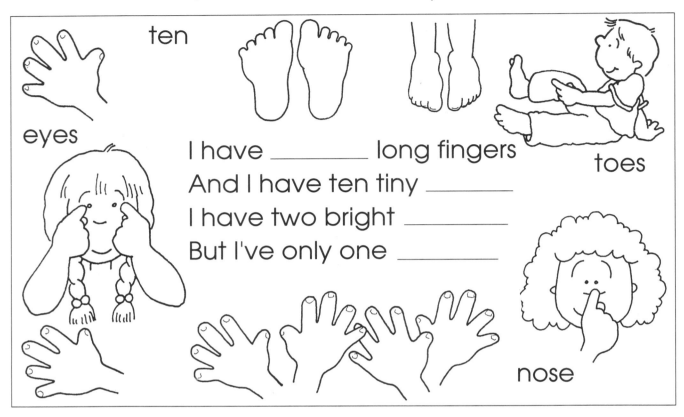

ten

eyes

toes

I have _____ long fingers
And I have ten tiny _____
I have two bright _____
But I've only one _____

nose

● Write the words in the spaces.

mat

I have a pretty little _____
She likes to sit upon a _____
And when I stroke her silky _____
My pretty little _____ will purr.

fur

cat

What will happen next? – 1

● Name _____

What will happen next? – 2

Make a puppet

Make a puppet

Name _____

Find the rhyme – 1

● Work with a partner. Choose a picture in a square.
Say the word. Can your partner find the rhyme?

cake

tie

car

rake

eye

star

cat

mouse

tree

rat

house

key

pear

fox

goat

chair

box

coat

Find the rhyme – 2

● Work with a partner. Choose a picture in a square.
Say the word. Can your partner find the rhyme?

bat

flag

frog

hat

bag

log

bell

straw

pen

peg

spoon

duck

egg

moon

truck

shell

door

hen

Build a nursery rhyme

● Can you put the rhyme in the right order? Cut out each part and build the rhyme.

One, two	buckle my shoe.
Five, six	pick up sticks.
Nine, ten	a big, fat hen.
Three, four	knock on the door.
Seven, eight	lay them straight.

Rebus rhyme – 1

● Say the rhyme. The pictures will help you.

 sat on a

Humpty Dumpty had a great fall.

All the King's

And all the 's   men

Couldn't put 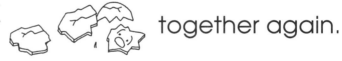 together again.

● Now the rhyme is jumbled up. Can you put it in the right order?

All the King's horses

Humpty Dumpty sat on a wall.

Couldn't put Humpty together again.

And all the King's men

Humpty Dumpty had a great fall.

Rebus rhyme – 2

● Say the rhyme. The pictures will help you.

Sat on a

Eating her

Down came a

Which sat down beside her

and frightened   away.

● Can you say this rhyme on your own?
● Now the rhyme is jumbled up. Can you put it in the right order?

| Sat on a tuffet, |
| And frightened Miss Muffet away. |
| Little Miss Muffet |
| Down came a spider |
| Eating her curds and whey. |
| Which sat down beside her |

Choose-your-own fairy story

● Choose the pictures to make the story.

Once upon a time there was a

who lived in a

One day, a

came along who

and the

turned into a

● Now read <u>your</u> story to a friend.

Odd one out – 1

● Read each line to your partner. Mark the odd one out.

not	hot	pot	log
hen	men	set	ten
red	had	bed	fed
met	hit	set	get
did	pin	win	tin
hop	mop	map	top
hid	hip	did	lid
lip	lap	hip	sip
bat	cat	fat	set
cap	pip	map	tap

Odd one out – 2

● Read each line to your partner. Mark the odd one out.

say	day	dog	may
dot	not	top	pot
pit	rip	fit	bit
ran	pan	pen	man
hat	hid	cat	mat
may	met	get	set
bad	dad	did	had
cog	fog	log	let
wet	tin	let	set
win	bin	big	pin

My favourite story

● Fill in the details and then explain your choice to your partners.

Title _____   Saddest part _____

Author _____   _____

Best character _____   Ending _____

Worst character _____   _____

Funniest part _____   _____

_____   _____

● Draw your favourite character here.

Scottish 5-14 Curriculum: English language			
Attainment outcome	Strand	Attainment target	Level
Reading	Reading for information	Find and use information specific to their needs from a range of informational and reference sources.	C
	Reading to reflect on the writer's ideas and craft	Read a variety of texts and show they understand the main ideas and can draw conclusions from the text.	C
	Awareness of genre	Identify a few obvious features of form and content in different types of text: stories, poems, dramatic texts, newspaper items, informational and reference texts.	C
	Knowledge about language	Show they know, understand and can use the terms: fiction, non-fiction, verse, paragraph.	C

Northern Ireland Curriculum: English

The activities in this book support the following requirements of the programme of study for KS2:

AT2: Reading
Pupils should be able to:
- read with some independence, concentration and understanding, a range of texts for enjoyment and learning;
- listen to and read stories, poems and other materials and engage with them in a variety of ways;
- use, with some independence, written materials, in print or on screen, to support their learning;
- show in writing and expression that there is some understanding of the way texts are structured;
- use a range of organisational devices to locate information for chosen purposes.

AT3: Writing
Pupils should be able to:
- produce stories and other forms of writing based on a variety of stimuli and reflecting all areas of the curriculum;
- show a sense of structure which is appropriate to the form of writing;
- write independently in a wider range of forms which vary according to purpose, topic and readership; in this context, pupils should demonstrate an ability to:
  - show a widening active vocabulary;
- present the chosen subject matter in a structured form; in this context, the pupils will show an ability to organise and structure appropriately what is written in order to make meaning clear to the reader;
- produce independently writing of various forms for a range of personal and curricular purposes; in this context they should:
  - vary their vocabulary and language according to purpose, context and reader;
- use structures and layout which take account of purpose and readership; in this context, demonstrate competence in choosing and using a language style appropriate to the task, in organising subject matter clearly and appropriately.